SERENA

I SPY

6 PICTURE RIDDLE BOOKS

Riddles by Jean Marzollo
Photographs by Walter Wick

I Spy Funny Teeth
I Spy a Dinosaur's Eye
I Spy a School Bus
I Spy a Scary Monster
I Spy a Penguin
I Spy Lightning in the Sky

Cartwheel
B·O·O·K·S ®

SCHOLASTIC INC.
New York Toronto London Auckland
Sydney Mexico City New Delhi Hong Kong

For Chalupa,
with great thanks to Dan
— J.M.

For Elizabeth Helt
— W.W.

I Spy Funny Teeth (978-0-439-58472-8); Text copyright © 2003 by Jean Marzollo. "Toy Chest," "Make Believe," "Odds & Ends," and "Cubbies" from *I Spy* © 1992 by Walter Wick; "Peanuts and Popcorn" and "The Laughing Clown" from *I Spy Fun House* © 1993 by Walter Wick; "A Whale of a Tale" and "The Hidden Clue" from *I Spy Mystery* © 1993 by Walter Wick; "Yikes!" from *I Spy Fantasy* © 1994 by Walter Wick; "Mapping" from *I Spy School Days* © 1995 by Walter Wick.

I Spy a Dinosaur's Eye (978-0-439-52471-1); Text copyright © 2003 by Jean Marzollo. "Tiny Toys," "Odds & Ends," "Toy Chest," and "At the Beach" from *I Spy* © 1992 by Walter Wick; "The Toy Box Solution" and "The Hidden Clue" from *I Spy Mystery* © 1993 by Walter Wick; "City Blocks" from *I Spy Fantasy* © 1994 by Walter Wick; "Patterns and Paint" from *I Spy School Days* © 1995 by Walter Wick; "A Secret Cupboard" from *I Spy Spooky Night* © 1996 by Walter Wick.

I Spy a School Bus (978-0-439-52473-5); Text copyright © 2003 by Jean Marzollo. "Tiny Toys," "Odds & Ends," "Bulletin Board," "At the Beach," and "Blocks" from *I Spy* © 1992 by Walter Wick; "The Mysterious Monster" and "A Whale of a Tale" from *I Spy Mystery* © 1993 by Walter Wick; "City Blocks" and "Yikes!" from *I Spy Fantasy* © 1994 by Walter Wick; "Mapping" from *I Spy School Days* © 1995 by Walter Wick.

I Spy a Scary Monster (978-0-439-68054-7); Text copyright © 2004 by Jean Marzollo. "Arts & Crafts" from *I Spy* © 1992 by Walter Wick; "Carnival Warehouse" from *I Spy Fun House* © 1993 by Walter Wick; "Masquerade" from *I Spy Mystery* © 1993 by Walter Wick; "Monster Workshop" and "Sand Castle" from *I Spy Fantasy* © 1994 by Walter Wick; "Storybook Theater" from *I Spy School Days* © 1995 by Walter Wick; "A Blazing Fire," "The Fountain," and "Ghost of the Night" from *I Spy Spooky Night* © 1996 by Walter Wick.

I Spy a Penguin (978-0-439-73862-0); Text copyright © 2005 by Jean Marzollo. "Flights of Fancy" and "Sweet Dreams" from *I Spy Fantasy* © 1994 by Walter Wick; "Blocks" and "Cubbies" from *I Spy* © 1992 by Walter Wick; "The Birthday Hunt," "The Hidden Clue," and "The Secret Note" from *I Spy Mystery* © 1993 by Walter Wick; "Peanuts and Popcorn" from *I Spy Fun House* © 1993 by Walter Wick; "The Library" from *I Spy Spooky Night* © 1996 by Walter Wick; "Sorting and Classifying" from *I Spy School Days* © 1995 by Walter Wick.

I Spy Lightning in the Sky (978-0-439-68052-3); Text copyright © 2005 by Jean Marzollo. Illustrations copyright © 1999 by Walter Wick. All images by Walter Wick taken from *I Spy Treasure Hunt*.

ISBN 978-0-545-27984-0

12 11 10 9 8 7 6 5 4 3 2 1   10 11 12 13 14 15/0
Printed in Singapore 46 • This compilation edition first printing, June 2010

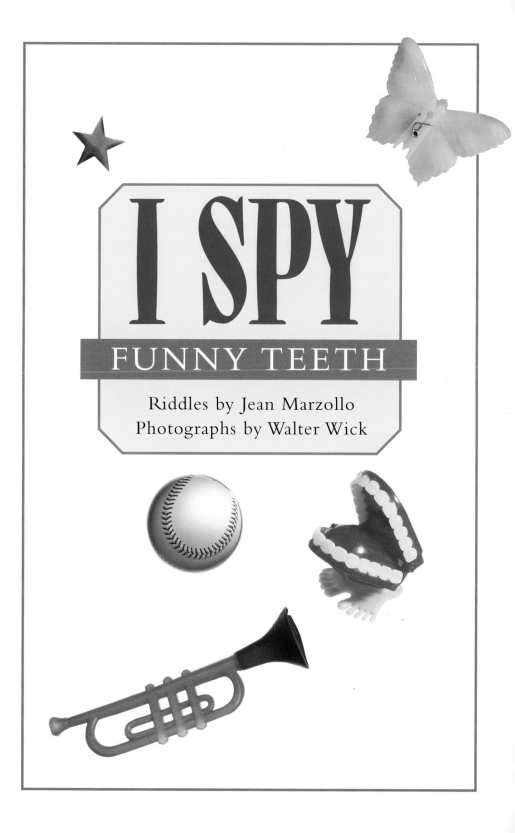

I SPY

FUNNY TEETH

Riddles by Jean Marzollo

Photographs by Walter Wick

I spy

a car,

a kazoo,

a horn,

a number game,

and a box of popcorn.

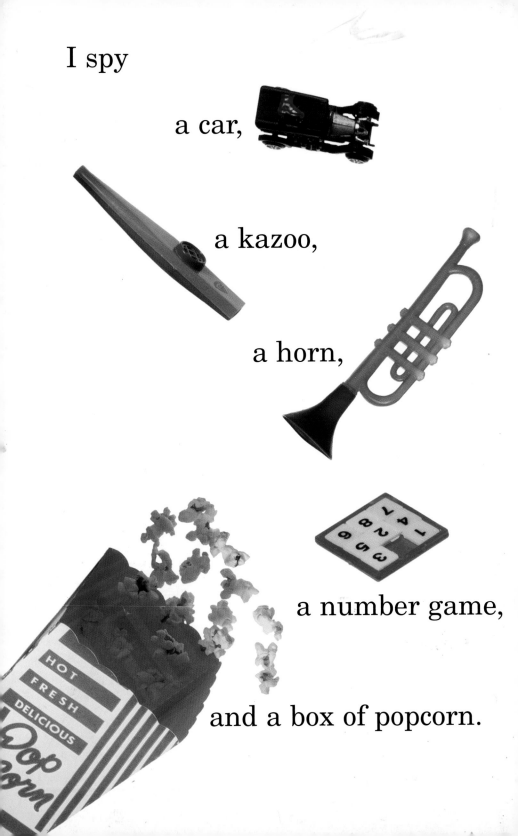

I spy

a tank,

  two baseballs,

a clock,

a frog in a truck,

and a blue wooden block.

I spy

a guitar,

 a fish,

a bow tie,

 a face,

an axe,

and a butterfly.

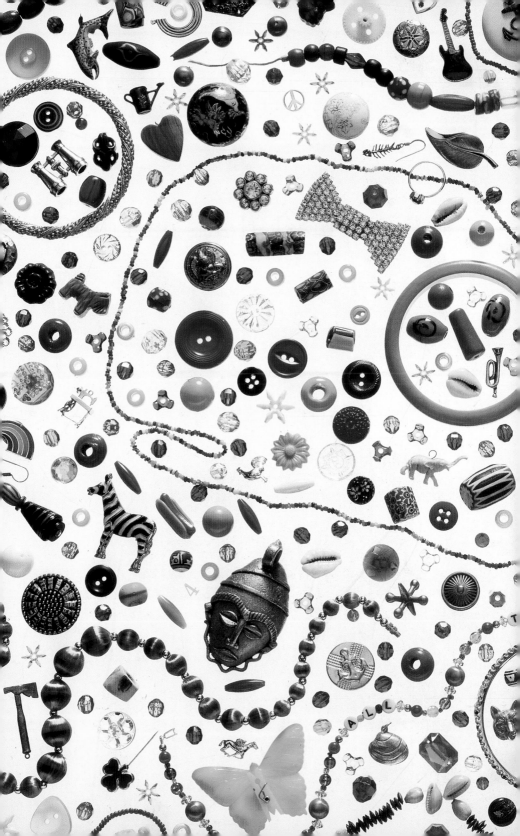

I spy

sunglasses,

a mask that's dark blue,

a clock,

a fan,

and a pink purse, too.

I spy

a green star,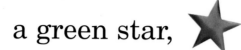

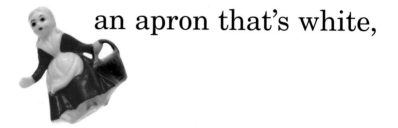 an apron that's white,

a truck,

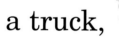 a jack,

and a red flashlight.

I spy

two gas pumps,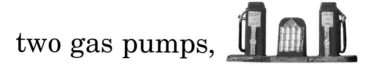

 a maze,

a bear,

four pink flowers,

and a clown's yellow hair.

I spy

a spoon,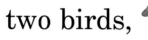

 a basket of fruit,

two birds,

 an S,

and a cowboy boot.

I spy

a giraffe,

 a marble,

 a king,

two googly eyes,

 and a blue-stone ring.

I spy

a domino,

 a big yellow Y,

funny white teeth,

and a red bow tie.

I spy

five hats,

three M's,

an E,

a musical note,

and a zebra Z.

I spy two matching words.

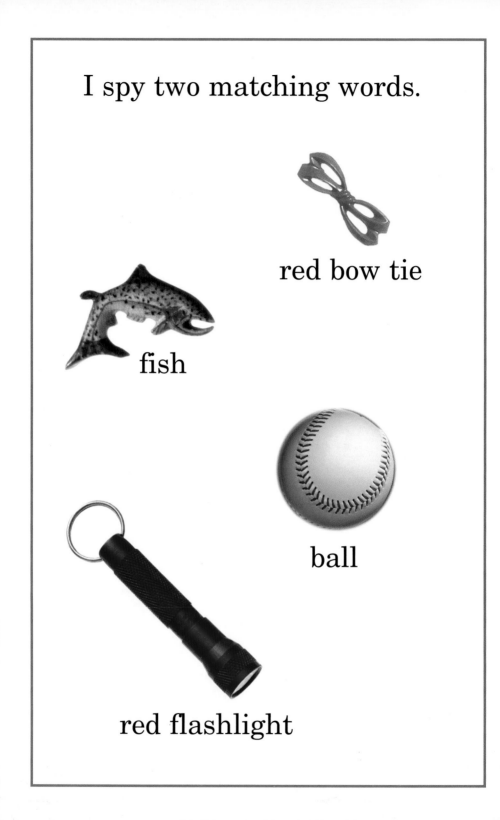

red bow tie

fish

ball

red flashlight

I spy two matching words.

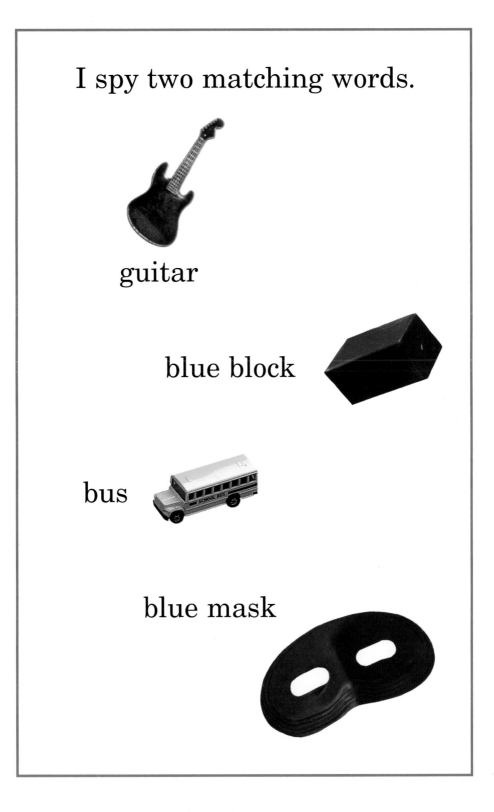

guitar

blue block

bus

blue mask

I spy two words that start
with the letter B.

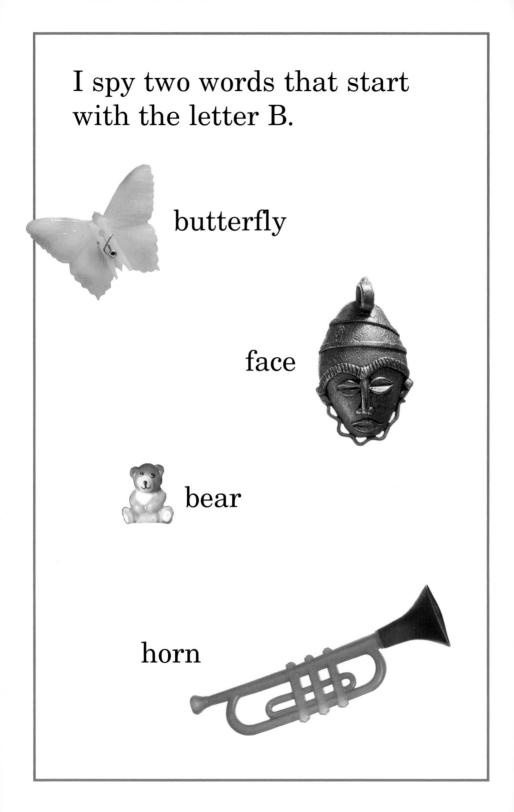

butterfly

face

bear

horn

I spy three words that start
with the letter P.

two gas pumps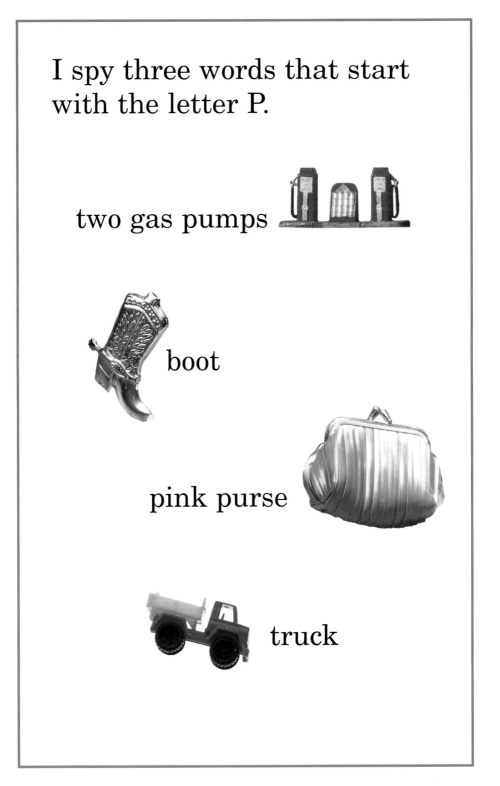

boot

pink purse

truck

I spy two words that end with the letter S.

teeth

two googly eyes

car

two birds

I spy two words that end with the letters CK.

jack

game

zebra

truck

I spy two words that rhyme.

yellow Y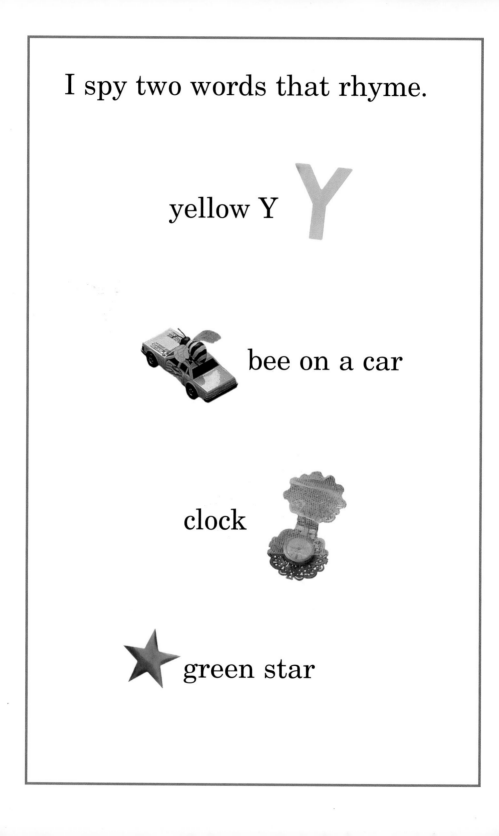

bee on a car

clock

green star

I spy two words that rhyme.

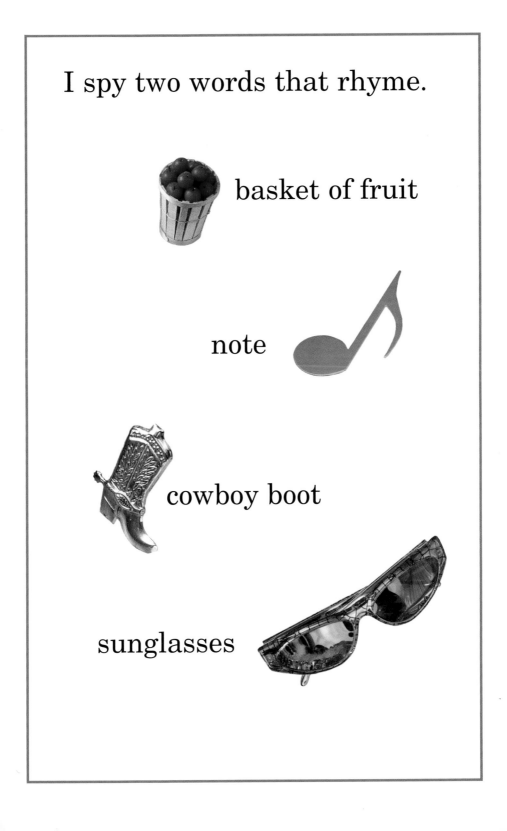

basket of fruit

note

cowboy boot

sunglasses

For Ziggy, with extra thanks to Dan
— J.M.

To Abigail Helt
— W.W.

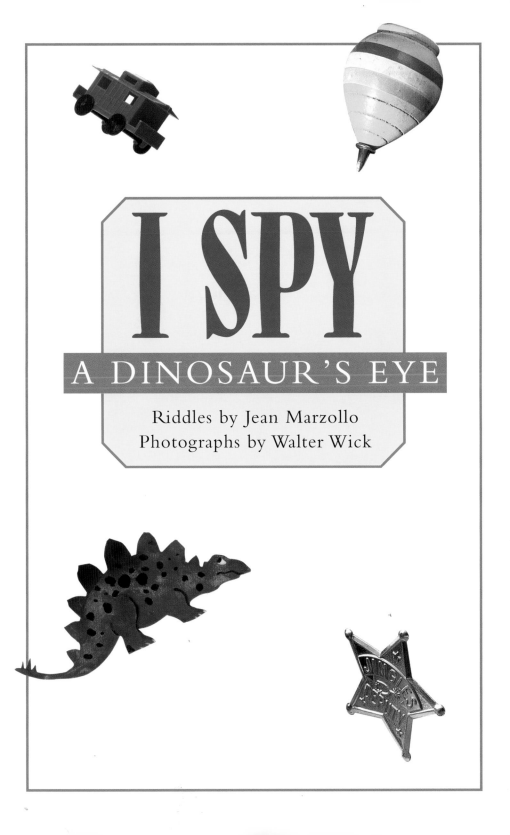

I SPY

A DINOSAUR'S EYE

Riddles by Jean Marzollo

Photographs by Walter Wick

I spy

a ball,

a bear,

a B,

and a very small

Statue of Liberty.

I spy

a palm tree,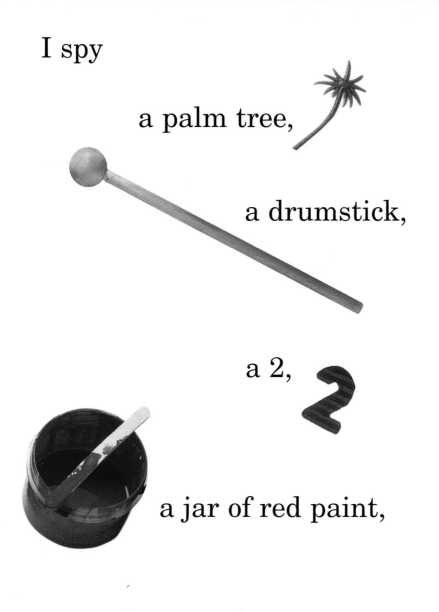

a drumstick,

a 2,

a jar of red paint,

and a cow that can moo.

I spy

an angel,

a dragon,

a Q,

an egg split in half,

and a hat that is blue.

I spy

a green light,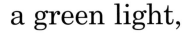

 two blocks,

a 2,

 an old toy ship,

and a 4 of bones, too.

I spy

a magnet,

a metal key,

a boat,

a barrette,

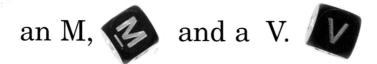an M, and a V.

I spy

a surfboard,

a rake,

a sail,

the letter A,

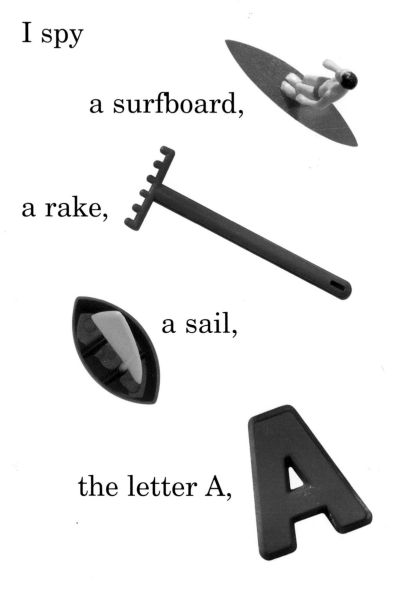

 and a frog in a pail.

I spy

a caboose,

 a dinosaur's eye,

a large yellow e,

and a plane that can fly.

I spy

a bulldozer,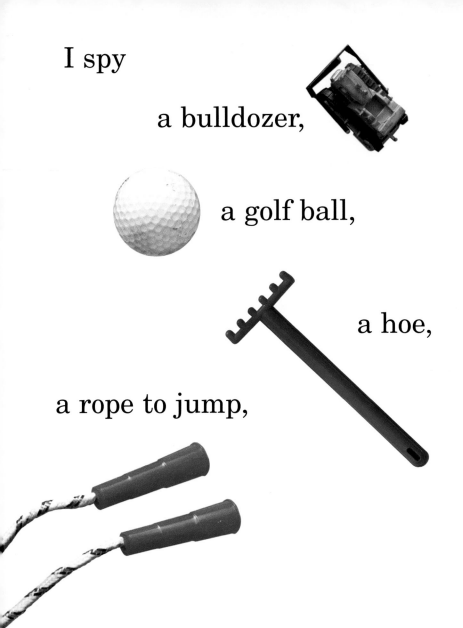

a golf ball,

a hoe,

a rope to jump,

and a man who can throw.

I spy

a rubber band

a bite,

 a J,

a deputy's badge,

 and the letter A.

I spy

a top,

a small saxophone,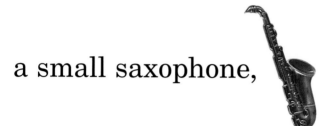

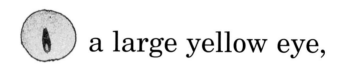 a large yellow eye,

and a horse all alone.

I spy two matching words.

small saxophone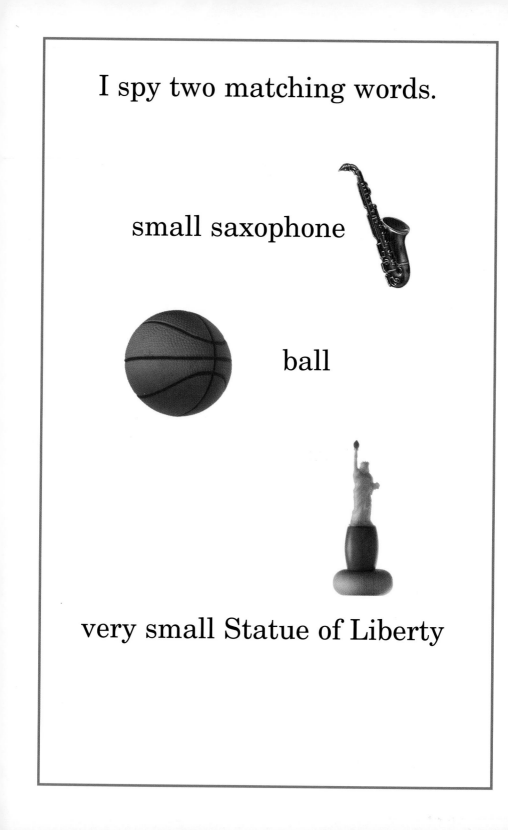

ball

very small Statue of Liberty

I spy two matching words.

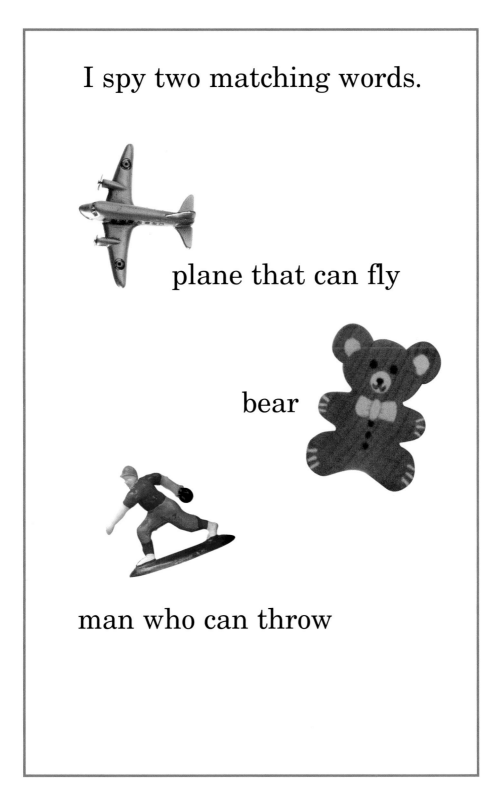

plane that can fly

bear

man who can throw

I spy two words that start with the letters DR.

drumstick

palm tree

dragon

I spy two words that start with the letter H.

hat that is blue

angel

horse all alone

I spy three words that end with the letter T.

 green light

magnet

boat

ball

I spy two words that end with the letter P.

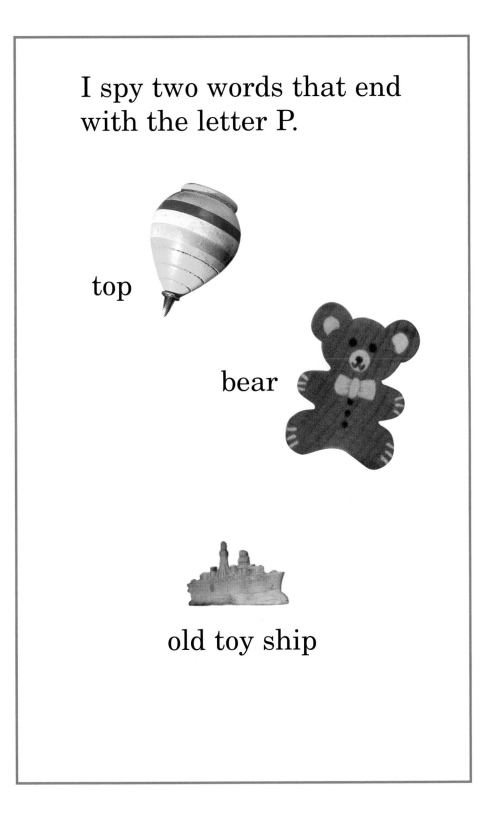

top

bear

old toy ship

I spy two words that rhyme.

palm tree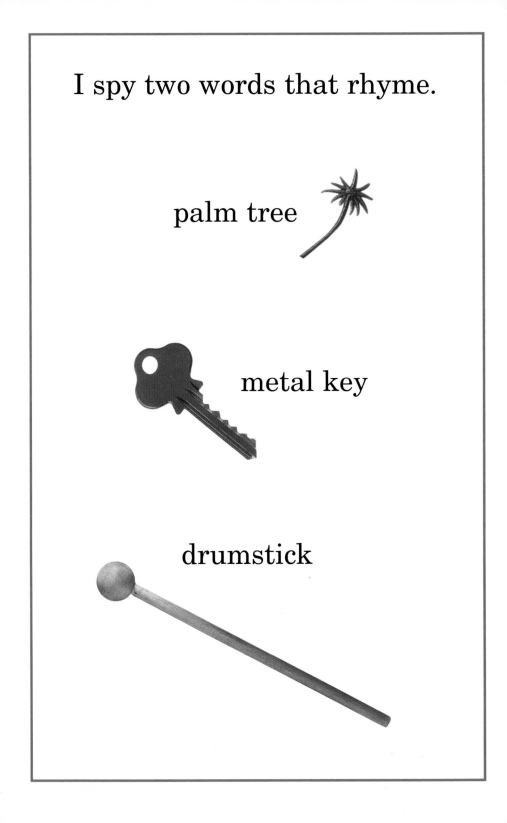

metal key

drumstick

I spy two words that rhyme.

cow that can moo

boat

hat

For Karin and Sam Rees,
with thanks to Dan
— J.M.

For Melanie Word
— W.W.

I SPY

A SCHOOL BUS

Riddles by Jean Marzollo
Photographs by Walter Wick

I spy

a bus,

 two trees,

a green star,

 a hopscotch game,

and a smile on a car.

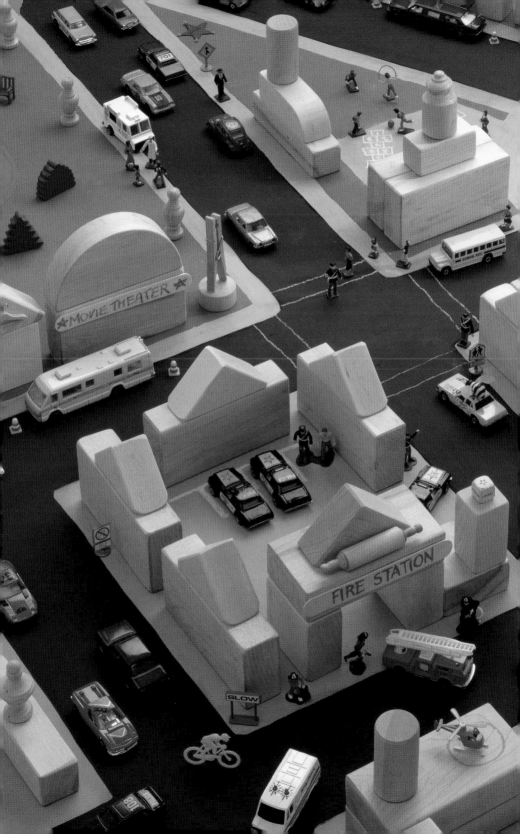

I spy glasses

 a lobster,

five fish,

 a chick in a boat,

 and a penny for a wish.

I spy
corn,

a surfer,

a pipe,

a pink stingray,

and a car with a stripe.

I spy

a screwdriver,

 a face that's small,

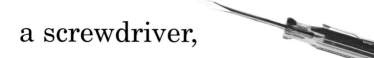

scissors,

a comb,

 and a little football.

I spy  a hammer,

a nut,

 a deer,

two little stars,

 and a glass
that is clear.

I spy

a green hat,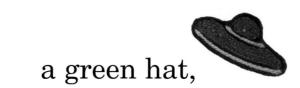

 a boxing glove,

a duck,

 and a rainbow
high above.

I spy

 five cards,

a button that's red,

 a ring,

a badge,

 and a crown for a head.

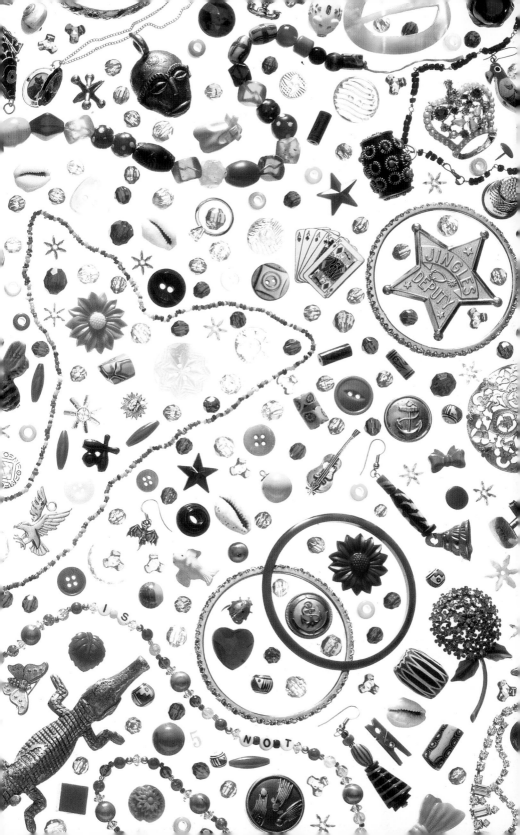

I spy

an eggbeater,

 a blue bowling pin,

a yellow fire hydrant,

and an orange tail fin.

BUMP

I spy

a timer,

 a frog,

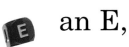 an E,

a yellow bus,

 and a wooden D.

I spy

a bike,

 a car with a 9,

 an 8,

and a truck
with MILK
on a sign.

I spy two matching words.

yellow fire
hydrant

 yellow bus

green star

I spy two matching words.

 face that's small

button that's red

pink stingray

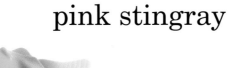

I spy two words that start with the letter C.

 corn

five cards

pipe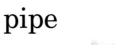

I spy two words that start with the letters GL.

boxing glove

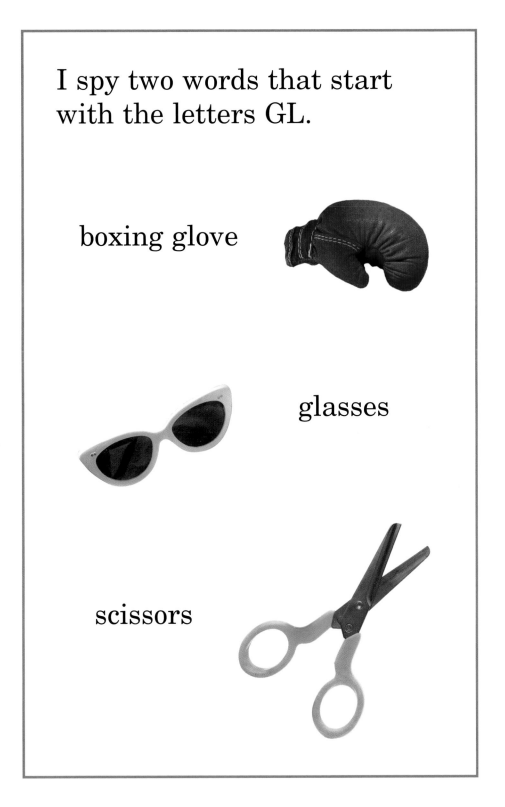

glasses

scissors

I spy two words that end with the letter N.

 orange tail fin

blue bowling pin

 football

I spy two words that end with the letters ER.

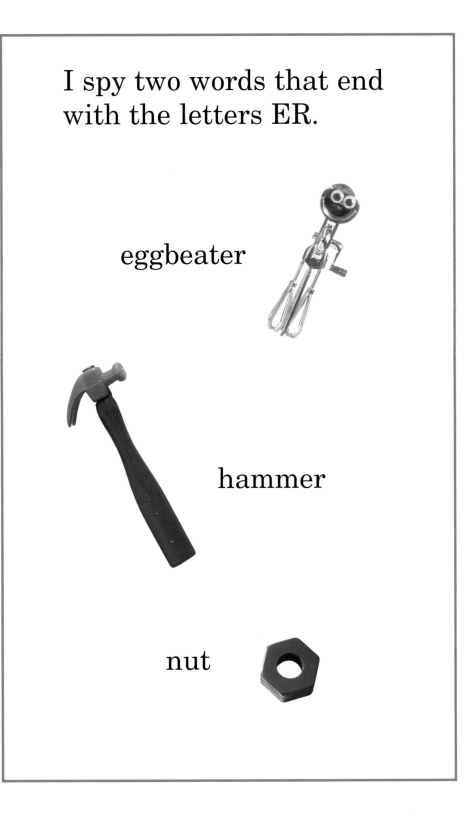

eggbeater

hammer

nut

I spy two words that rhyme.

duck

truck

hat

I spy two words that rhyme.

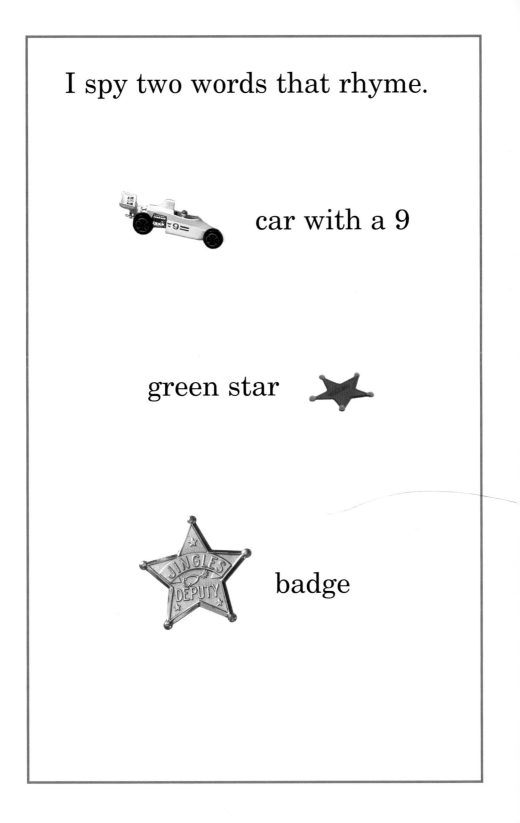

car with a 9

green star

badge

For Peter and his cousin Dan
—J.M.

For Jack Griffin
— W.W.

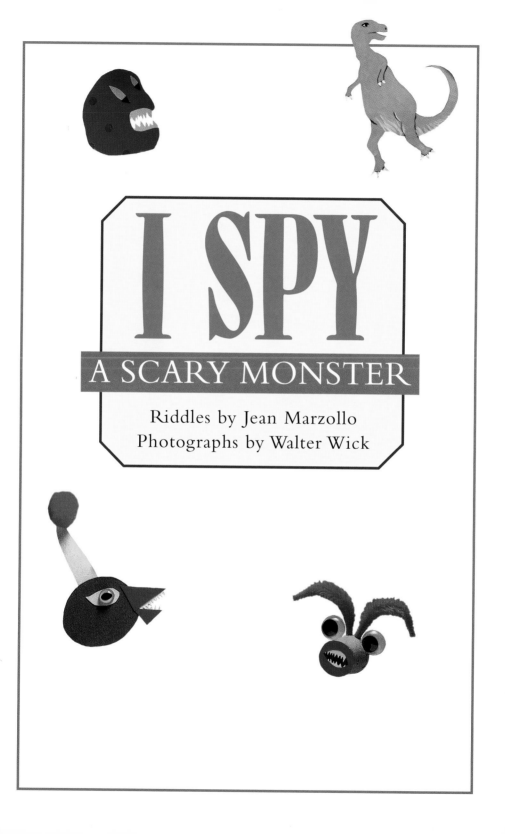

I SPY

A SCARY MONSTER

Riddles by Jean Marzollo

Photographs by Walter Wick

I spy

two paint jars,

snaky blue hair,

two horns,

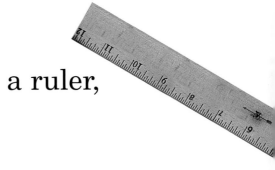

a ruler,

 and a little black bear.

I spy

a skeleton,

 a set for tea,

 two fish,

a ship,

and a leaf from a tree.

I spy

a witch,

a fancy chair,

a monster tree,

and orange hair.

I spy

a crossbow,

a shield white and red,

 two small flags,

and a sand-dragon's head.

I spy

a black cat,

a green crocodile,

a ladder,

a pail,

and a lion's smile.

I spy

a tiger,

two D's,

three O's,

a colorful pencil,

and T-Rex's toes.

I spy

a red eye,

a spider,

a spoon,

a spooky turtle monster,

and a bright full moon.

I spy

a paintbrush,

two yellow laces,

a little green gear,

and five toothy faces.

I spy

a cork,

 a shoe that's blue,

 two bears,

two dogs,

 and a pudgy pig, too.

I spy

a fork,

a dinosaur,

an E,

a frog,

and a ghost that's looking at me!

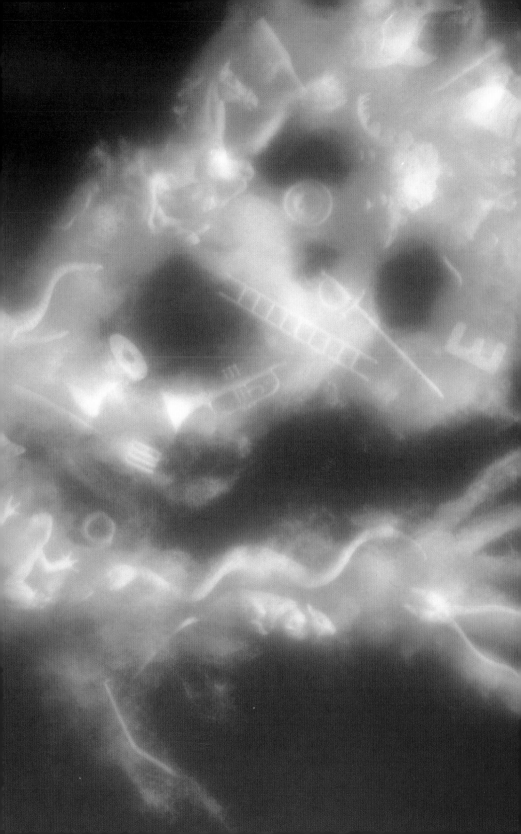

I spy two matching words.

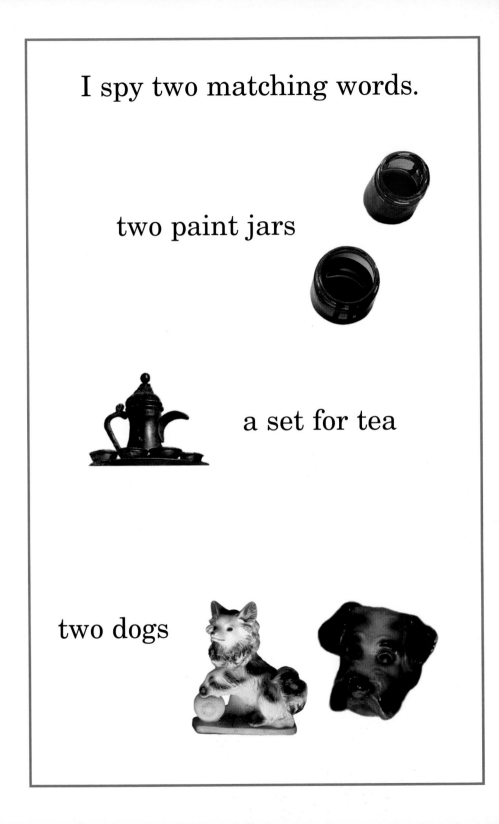

two paint jars

a set for tea

two dogs

I spy two matching words.

a ship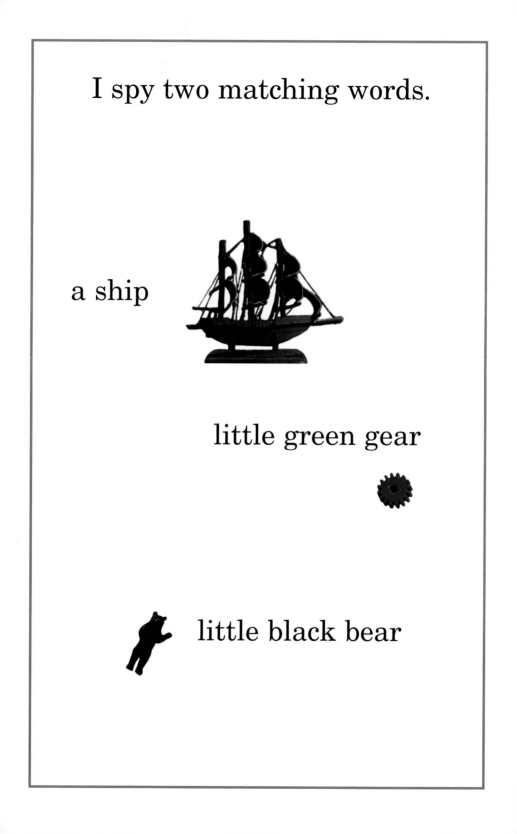

little green gear

little black bear

I spy two words that start with the letter M.

spooky
turtle monster

orange hair

 bright full moon

I spy two words that start with the letters CR.

two small flags

crocodile

crossbow

I spy two words that end with a silent letter E.

a toothy face

a ladder

lion's smile

I spy two words that end with the letters SH.

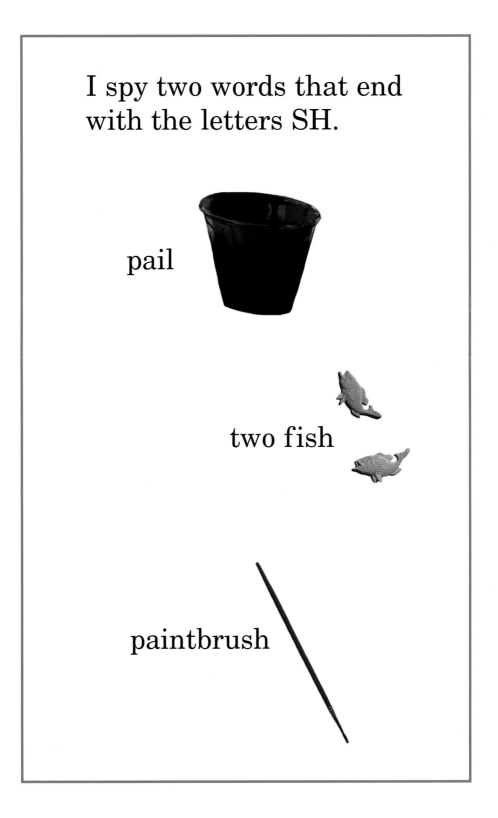

pail

two fish

paintbrush

I spy two words that rhyme.

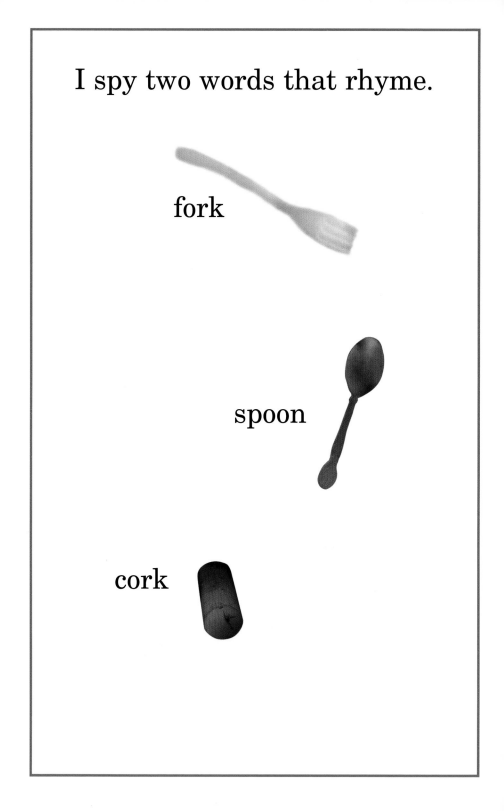

fork

spoon

cork

I spy two words that rhyme.

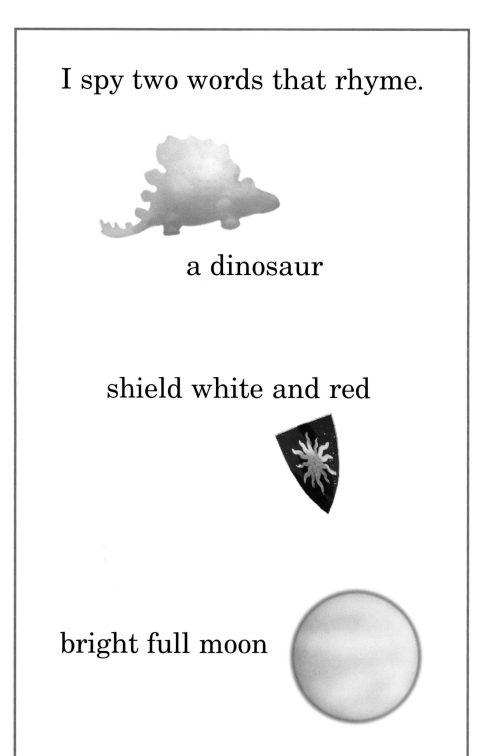

a dinosaur

shield white and red

bright full moon

For Hartman, Hirshey,
Mansfield, McGuirk, & Stokes
— J.M.

For Oscar Mindich
— W.W.

I SPY
A PENGUIN

Riddles by Jean Marzollo
Photographs by Walter Wick

I spy

 red lips,

two rings,

 an ax,

a turtle,

 a ship,

and three silver jacks.

I spy

two trucks,

 a penguin,

a pig,

 a horse lying down,

and a number
that's big.

I spy

a ballerina,

a bow,

a striped cat,

an ice-cream treat,

and a small straw hat.

STEEP
GRADE

I spy

 a seashell,

a dog,

five stars,

a colorful plane,

  and two old cars.

I spy

a trunk,

 two antlers,

a die,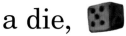

a zebra,

 a basket,

and a lonely eye.

I spy

a panda,

 a purple unicorn,

a lunch box,

a chair,

and an ear of corn.

I spy

a clown,

 a cat,

 an O,

a castle pin,

 and a yellow bow.

I spy

a cactus,

 four bowling pins,

a pretty black shell,

 and yellow fish fins.

I spy

an anteater,

 a tasty hot dog,

a compass,

 a lock,

and a spotted frog.

I spy

 a puppy's tongue,

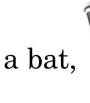 a bat,

 a V,

 a little blue car,

 an N,

and a C.

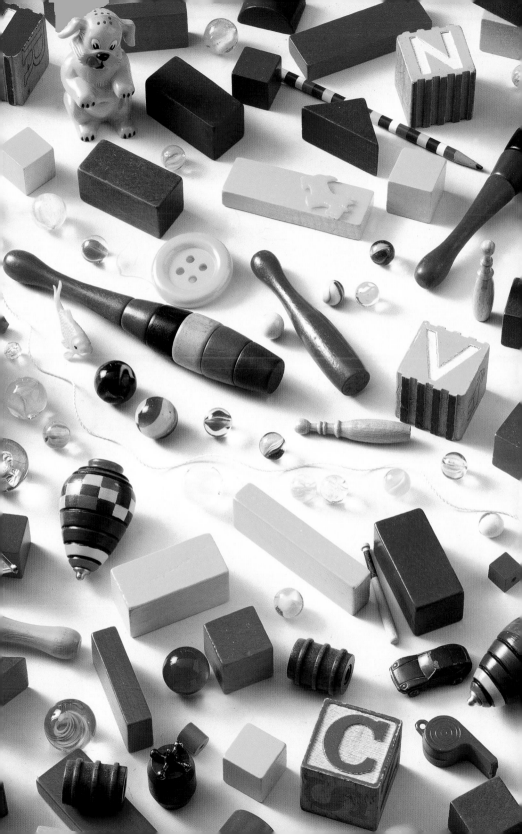

I spy two matching words.

yellow bow

yellow fish fins

spotted frog

I spy two matching words.

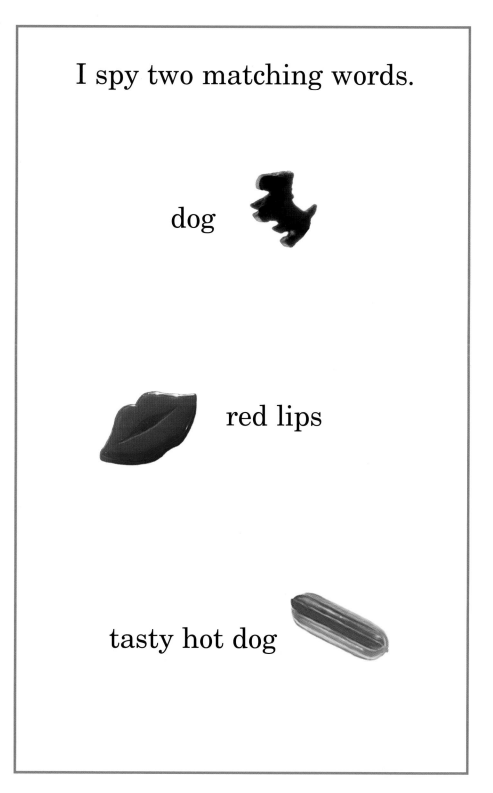

dog

red lips

tasty hot dog

I spy two words that start with the letter L.

horse lying down

 striped cat

 lonely eye

I spy two words that start with the letters STR.

 striped cat

ballerina

small straw hat

I spy two words that end with the letter N.

penguin

ice-cream treat

clown costume

I spy two words that end
with the letters CKS.

 three silver jacks

ear of corn

two trucks

I spy two words that rhyme.

dog

zebra

frog

I spy two words that rhyme.

five stars

two old cars

purple unicorn

For Allen and his cousin Dave
—J.M.

For Maya Griffin
— W.W.

I SPY
LIGHTNING IN THE SKY

Riddles by Jean Marzollo
Photographs by Walter Wick

I spy

 a truck,

a lighthouse light,

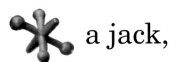 a jack,

and a lightning bolt
at night.

I spy

a tiny toy cannon,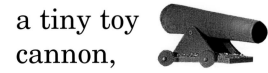

 a 3,

a brown starfish,

 and two shells from the sea.

I spy

a stop sign,

 a wet blue duck,

Sharky's shack,

 and a yellow truck.

I spy

a shell,

two oars,

 LOST CAT,

a fish,

and a biker in a red hat.

I spy

a screw,

 a pair of wings,

a key in a jar,

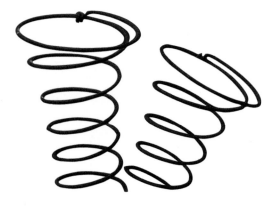

and two large springs.

I spy

a ladder,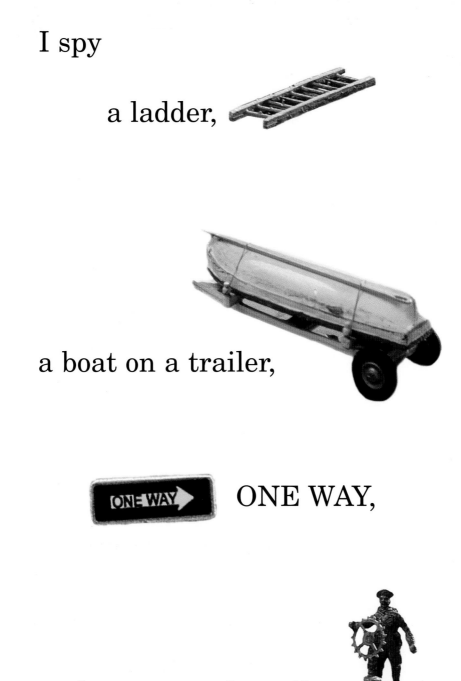

a boat on a trailer,

ONE WAY,

and a statue of a sailor.

I spy

a starfish,

a seagull,

a seal,

a magnifying glass,

and a silver
ship's wheel.

I spy

an arrow,

a pail on a string,

a furry groundhog,

and a tire swing.

I spy

an oar,

a ship,

a plane,

TOW-AWAY ZONE,

and a rusty chain.

I spy

 a trash can,

a red suitcase,

 two bobby pins,

and a president's face.

I spy two matching words.

tiny toy cannon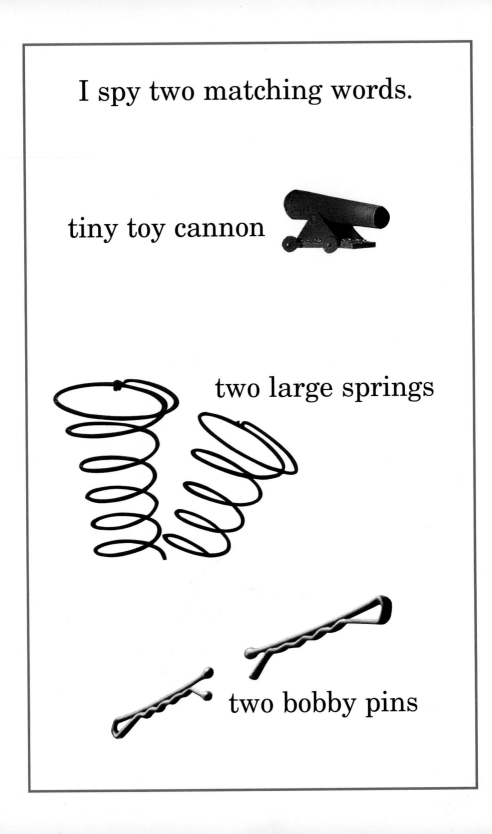

two large springs

two bobby pins

I spy two matching words.

statue of a sailor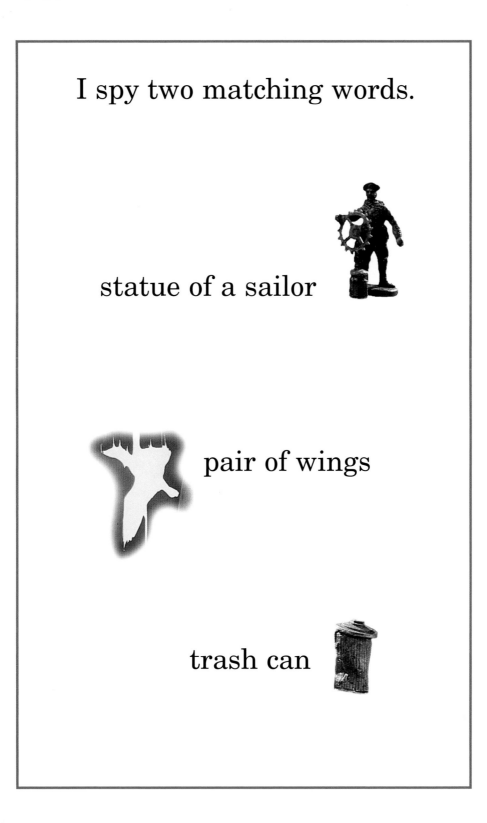

pair of wings

trash can

I spy two words that start with the letter S.

 seal

suitcase

 groundhog

I spy two words that start with the letter L.

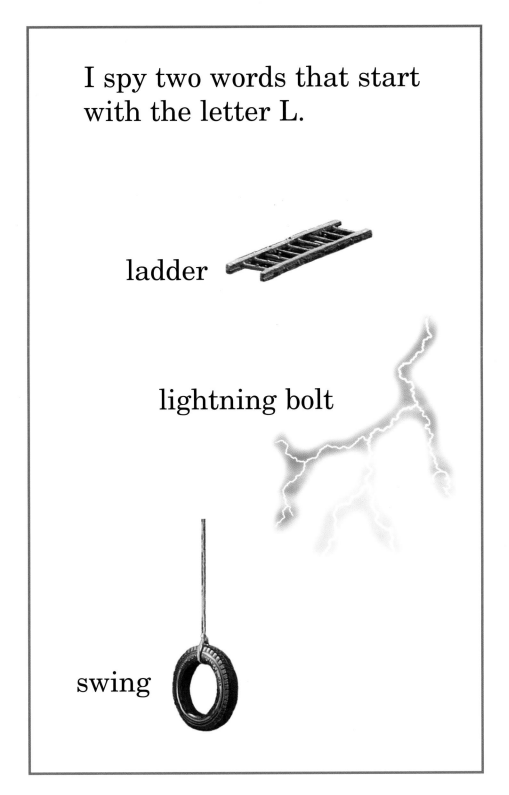

ladder

lightning bolt

swing

I spy two words that end with the letters LL.

seagull

shell

wheel

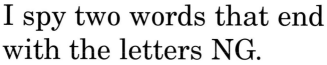

I spy two words that end with the letters NG.

pail on a string

tire swing

statue

I spy two words that rhyme.

plane

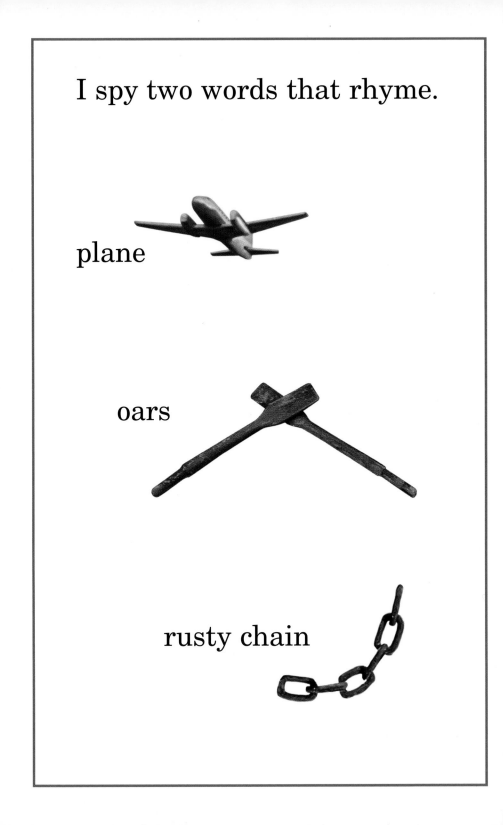

oars

rusty chain

I spy two words that rhyme.

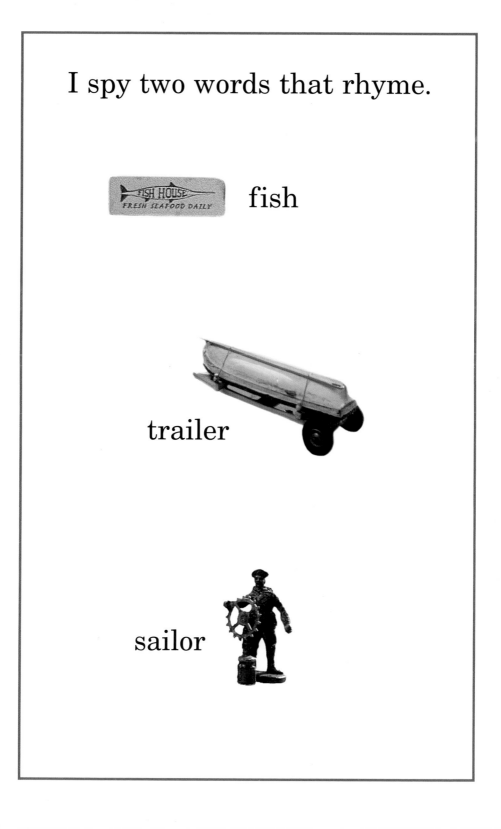

fish

trailer

sailor